© Kevin Chettle

Protecting people who have a learning disability from abuse

Induction Award

Supporting people who have a learning disability

Jackie Pountney

www.bild.org.uk
✓ Information and support
✓ Useful weblinks
✓ 24 hour online ordering

0845 370 0067

www.harcourt.co.uk
✓ Free online support
✓ Useful weblinks
✓ 24 hour online ordering

01865 888118

working together **bild** Heinemann

Heinemann is an imprint of Harcourt Education Limited, a company incorporated in England and Wales, having its registered office: Halley Court, Jordan Hill, Oxford OX2 8EJ. Registered company number: 3099304

www.harcourt.co.uk

Heinemann is the registered trademark of Harcourt Education Limited

Text © BILD 2007

First published 2007

12 11 10 09 08 07

10 9 8 7 6 5 4 3 2 1

British Library Cataloguing in Publication Data is available from the British Library on request.

ISBN 978 0 435500 03 0

Edited by TAG Publishing Services
Designed and typeset by 𝄃 Tek-Art, Croydon Surrey
Original illustrations © Harcourt Education Limited 2007
Cover illustration © Kevin Chettle
Printed in the UK by Scotprint

Acknowledgements
The author and publisher would like to thank the following individuals and organisations for permission to reproduce photographs: Page 2 – © Harcourt Education Ltd. Jules Selmes; page 17 – © Lauren Shear/Science Photo Library; page 31 – © photos.com; page 35 – © istockphoto/absolute_100; page 43 – © Leslie Garland Picture Library/Alamy.

Every effort has been made to contact copyright holders of material reproduced in this book. Any omissions will be rectified in subsequent printings if notice is given to the publishers.

Websites
The websites used in this book were correct and up to date at the time of publication. It is essential for tutors to preview each website before using it in class so as to ensure that the URL is still accurate, relevant and appropriate. We suggest that tutors bookmark useful websites and consider enabling students to access them through the school/college/satellite centre/service provider intranet.

Contents

About the British Institute of Learning Disabilities

The British Institute of Learning Disabilities (BILD) is committed to improving the quality of life for people with a learning disability by involving them and their families in all aspects of our work, working with government and public bodies to achieve full citizenship, undertaking beneficial research and development projects and helping service providers to develop and share good practice.

BILD Publications is the imprint of:
British Institute of Learning Disabilities
Campion House
Green Street
Kidderminster
Worcestershire DY10 1JL
Telephone: 01562 723010
Fax: 01562 723029
Email: enquiries@bild.org.uk
Website: www.bild.org.uk

BILD Publications are distributed by:
BookSource
50 Cambuslang Road
Cambuslang
Glasgow G32 8NB
Telephone: 0845 370 0067
Fax: 0845 370 0068

For a publications catalogue with details of all BILD books and journals and for information about learning and qualifications services telephone 01562 723010, email enquiries@bild.org.uk or visit the BILD website www.bild.org.uk

Acknowledgements

I would like to thank the following people who have provided invaluable information and advice in writing this book:

- Denise Badger from People in Action
- Selina Bates from People in Action
- Stephen Dale from Staffordshire County Council
- Carol Draper from People in Action
- James Gulliver from People in Action
- Cathy James from Public Concern at Work
- Helen McGill-Kerr from People in Action
- Joseph Ngui from People in Action
- Neville Parkes from University of Worcester
- Andrew Strawbridge from Humber and East Riding Mental Health Trust
- Sue Sugars from People in Action

I would also like to thank Simon Bickerton, Robina Mallett and Nick Smith for their comments on drafts of this book and my colleagues from BILD, especially Lesley Barcham and Alan Martin.

We gratefully acknowledge the help of Kevin Chettle for permission to reproduce his paintings on the cover and title page. The paintings are a moving account of his life in a long-stay institution. Kevin now lives in the community and earns his living through giving lectures and selling his paintings which can be purchased through Advocacy in Action, telephone 01159 470780.

About the author

Jackie Pountney has worked with people with learning disabilities for most of her working life, firstly with Birmingham Social Services Department in the early 1980s and then in City College, Birmingham. When the LDAF qualification was introduced in 2001 she began to teach support workers as well. She has worked at BILD since 2004, supporting organisations to offer learning disability qualifications to their staff. She co-authored *Not behind the bikeshed*, a resource pack for teaching health and social education to people with learning disabilities, and worked with RoSPA to develop road safety training materials designed for children and adults with learning disabilities.

Introduction

induction
a period of learning, shortly after starting a new job or volunteering placement

service
the provision of social care support for a person that could be in their own home, their local community or in a residential home or similar place

family carer
a relative of a person with learning disabilities who has an interest in their well-being

direct payments
a way for people to organise their own social care support by receiving funding direct from their council, following an assessment of their needs

abuse
a violation of a person's human rights by any other person or persons. Anyone can experience abuse. It can be one single act, or repeated acts. It happens when someone either deliberately or unknowingly causes harm or endangers life or rights

This book is for anyone beginning work with people with a learning disability. It is one of four books that will provide you with all the information you need during your **induction**. It will help you to find out more about the lives of people with learning disabilities, the **service** you work for and what it means to be a social care worker or volunteer. It will also be useful for personal assistants, volunteers and **family carers**, as well as for the growing number of people who are now managing their own support with money they receive through **direct payments** and individual budgets.

Learning disability qualifications

Common Induction Standards

All new workers in social care jobs need to know about a number of important topics during the first few weeks and months in their new job. What you need to know has been decided by Skills for Care, the strategic development organisation for the adult social care workforce in England. The topics have been set out in their Common Induction Standards (CIS). Your employer will provide a detailed induction programme that will cover:

- listening to people with learning disabilities and their families
- communicating effectively
- working safely
- your organisation's policies and procedures
- your role as a learning disability worker
- recognising and responding to **abuse** and neglect
- the principles of care.

The four induction books that cover all the CIS topics are:

- *Principles of learning disability support*
- *Your role as a learning disability worker*
- *Health and safety in a learning disability service*
- *Protecting people who have a learning disability from abuse*

The Induction Award

As well as covering all the Skills for Care Common Induction Standards topics, the four books in this series also meet the requirements of the Induction Award: Supporting People who have a Learning Disability, a nationally recognised qualification appropriate for people who work in services that support people with learning disabilities.

The Induction Award helps new workers to develop knowledge and understanding. This series of books relating to the Common Induction Standards links to the Induction Award at levels 2 and 3.

Protecting people who have a learning disability from abuse covers all the learning needed for one Induction Award unit at levels 2 and 3. Induction Award accreditation for your induction learning will be helpful in your career in supporting people with learning disabilities because:

* you will have gained certificates for achieving a national qualification
* the knowledge and understanding you have gained during your induction will help you to move on to an NVQ qualification in health and social care.

NVQ in health and social care

The National Vocational Qualifications (NVQs) in health and social care are the recognised qualifications for the entire social care sector in England, Wales and Northern Ireland, including services that support people with a learning disability. In Scotland these qualifications are known as Scottish Vocational Qualifications (SVQs). NVQs assess your competence (knowledge, skills and abilities) in your job.

By completing your induction and the four Induction Award units that link to the Common Induction Standards you will be well on the way to completing your NVQ in health and social care.

As you progress from being a new worker to a qualified and experienced worker, your path of learning and qualifications could therefore look something like the diagram on the next page.

Time in job	Learning and experience	Assessment and qualifications
First 12 weeks	**Training related to Common Induction Standards**	• **Induction Award related to Common Induction Standards** • **Underpinning knowledge for NVQ core units covered and assessed**
3–9 months	**Additional learning and experience about supporting people with learning disabilities**	• **Additional units or knowledge sets** • **All the underpinning knowledge for the core NVQ units covered and assessed**
9 months +	**Ongoing learning and development of skills**	• **Assessment of competence for NVQ**
After successfully completing your NVQ	**Ongoing learning focused on the people you are supporting and their needs**	• **Possible progression to other learning disability specific units or knowledge sets**

▲ A possible path of learning and qualifications for new support workers

Working with people with learning disabilities, family carers and support workers

From day one in your work with people with learning disabilities it is important that you listen carefully to what the people you support are saying to you about their interests, needs and the support you will be providing. In researching and writing this book the author has worked closely with people with learning disabilities and has sought information about people's experiences and their views on what new workers need to know and do. Their contributions are woven throughout these books. The author has also consulted with new and experienced support workers and family carers.

Confidentiality and consent

As you work through the activities in this book, you may wish to include the person you support by, for example, talking with them about their life and using the information in an assignment. It is really important to obtain the consent of the person if you plan to include them in this way. Discuss your organisation's **confidentiality policy** with your line manager if you are unsure what to do.

Language and labels

Ideally we should call people by their name and not label them according to their age, ethnicity, religion, disability or indeed for any other reason. We should always see the person first and not the labels that others attach to them. However, there are times when labels, no matter how much we may dislike them, are used by all of us and for all of us, for example, students, teenagers, senior citizens, patients, claimants, fans, etc.

It has been discussed for many years how we should describe people with learning disabilities. Over time, the language we use changes because terms come to have new or different meanings or because people object to the labels that are used to describe them. It is important that we are sensitive to people's concerns about the labels that others might use to describe them.

Throughout this book the terms 'people with a learning disability' or 'people with learning disabilities' are used as these are the terms most commonly found in health and social care settings. Some organisations, including ones run by people with learning disabilities, prefer the term 'people with learning difficulties', which is also used in schools and colleges. The term 'social care worker' or 'support worker' is generally used for paid members of staff.

Those employed directly to provide social care support for people with a learning disability are generally referred to as 'personal assistants'. The word 'service' is used to refer to the workplace situation, whether this is supported living, day opportunities, community support or residential and nursing care. The word 'organisation' is used to refer to agencies that run services. Other terms that may not be clear are explained as they arise in the text or in the glossary.

How the book is organised

This book is interactive. As well as reading, you will be asked to think about examples of support given to people with learning disabilities, give your own ideas, talk to colleagues and try out some of the activities.

> **confidentiality**
> *concerning things that need to be kept private*

> **policy**
> *a statement or plan of action that clearly sets out an organisation's position or approach on a particular issue and tells staff what should be done in the circumstances*

In the next section you will find **Study skills advice** to help you get the most from the time you spend studying and to ensure that it will be enjoyable and successful.

Each chapter contains the following features.

Learning outcomes. There are seven learning outcomes to the Protecting People who have a Learning Disability from Abuse units at levels 2 and 3 of the Induction Award: Supporting People who have a Learning Disability. Each of these learning outcomes is given a chapter in this book.

 Activities provide exercises designed to encourage you to apply what you have learned to your work situation.

 Key points summarise the main ideas in the chapter.

 Thinking points are suggestions for you to reflect on your own experiences and how they may affect the support you provide.

 Scenarios are brief studies illustrating ideas or issues covered in the chapter.

 Policy references give information about the key policies, laws and guidance that directly affect you as a social care worker and that set out what you have to do in your work.

 Examples provide detailed studies illustrating the key ideas covered in the chapter. These are designed to develop your ability to discuss and think more deeply about the topics as you cover them, provide an opportunity to reflect on the type of support you and your colleagues give to the people with learning disabilities you work with and give an overview of how they apply in your work on a day-to-day basis.

At the end of the book you will find the following sections.

Commentaries on the examples provides detailed feedback for each of the examples from the end of each chapter to help you review your work on each once it is completed.

Glossary provides explanations of technical words or phrases used in this book in plain, jargon-free English. These words are also explained in the margins, close to where they first appear in the book.

NVQ mapping provides detailed references showing the links to NVQ health and social care qualifications.

Resources lists the key publications, DVDs and websites to refer to if you want additional information on any of the topics covered in this book.

Study skills advice

We all vary in how we study and learn. Some people prefer to study in short bursts, spreading their learning over a long period. Others prefer more sustained periods of concentration. Some of us like to study early in the day and others don't start until late in the evening. No one way of working is better than another. You should find a way that suits you. The following guidelines will help you to get the most from the time you spend studying and help to ensure that it will be enjoyable and successful.

The right environment

You will study better in a quiet room that is free from distractions and where you will be undisturbed. Make sure that your seat is comfortable and supportive and that you have enough working space to spread out your study materials. Good lighting will make reading easier and help prevent your eyes from getting tired.

Identifying and using resources

You may find some of the topics covered in this book interest you so much that you want to find out further information about them. You can find information about working with people with learning disabilities from:

- books
- newspapers
- magazines
- journals
- websites
- television
- colleagues
- people with learning disabilities.

It's a good idea to keep a record of your resources. You could cut out and keep newspaper or magazine articles and make a note of websites you have visited or television programmes you have watched. You will need to have a good filing system so that you can organise these resources to enable you to find what you need quickly.

Reading

We read for many different reasons and purposes. The reading you do for your studies is likely to be very different from reading for leisure. Probably the most important difference is the way you work through the text. When you read a novel, you will usually open it at the first page and read through to the end. This is known as 'passive reading' because you are reading everything without question. When you are studying, you may read only one chapter, or use the index to find information on one subject that is located in various places through the book. This is known as 'active reading' because you are finding the answer to a question.

When you are studying, it's a good idea to give yourself targets so that you read more effectively. You could ask yourself questions such as:

- Do I really need to know this information?
- Do I need to know some of this information?
- Is this nothing at all to do with what I need to know?

As you go through the text, have a pen near you to take notes, or a highlighter or Post-its to mark key points. This will help you to sift out information which will be useful to you.

Reading styles

Once you have established the purpose of your reading you can identify the style of reading most suited to your task. The most commonly used types of reading are:

- **Skimming** involves going through a text quickly at about two to three times your normal reading speed. Look at the index, chapter headings, introduction and conclusion, as well as looking at the first line of each paragraph. This is a useful technique for deciding whether the book contains any information that is useful to you.
- **Scanning** is useful when you know exactly what you are looking for, such as a telephone number or place name. You find the word or phrase you are looking for and then follow the text.
- **Search reading** is used to look for key words and phrases which will help you find specific information. Look in the index to see where you will find key words and topics. Then locate these in the publication by scanning though until you find the words or phrases you are interested in.
- **Receptive reading** is where you need to have a good general understanding or to find out accurately what has been written. When reading receptively you need time to pay close attention to the text, think about what you have read and perhaps make notes.

Taking notes

One of the most important skills to develop through your studies is the ability to make clear and concise notes. You can make notes in training sessions or as you read a book or article or watch a television programme. Making notes helps you to understand a topic and identify its key points.

A common mistake when taking notes is to write everything down. You can make more useful notes by thinking about what you are looking for before you start reading the material or listening to the presentation. Produce notes that are relevant only to what you are looking for and try not to be sidetracked by writing down information you don't need.

There are different ways of taking notes. You should choose a method that suits you. Bear in mind that you will have to remember what they mean later on. Some ways of taking notes are:

- a short summary of the main points
- numbered points or structured lists
- a list of headings and subheadings
- mind maps, patterns and spider diagrams
- shorthand
- key points.

You should write down where you have taken your notes from, for example, the publication or the website. If you use the information in an assignment you will need to say where you got it from. This is known as *referencing*. Use highlighter pens where you can to highlight the main points. Post-it notes are useful to mark important information that you can return to later on.

Organising your time

Spending time planning your studies can be helpful. Firstly, you can avoid a last-minute rush to meet deadlines. Secondly, if you plan how you are going to approach each task you are more likely to carry out each stage effectively and produce a higher quality piece of work. The key stages of organising your time effectively are:

- **Being realistic** is important if you want to organise your time effectively. To work out how much time you actually have to study each week you should ask yourself what other commitments you have that take up time, such as:
  - work
  - family
  - social events

- **Planning ahead** is essential. You will need to ask yourself a number of questions:
  - What exactly is involved?
  - How long will it take?
  - When will you do it?
  - How will you do it?
  - What is the deadline for completion?

- **Organising your studies** carefully will enable you to make the best use of the time you have available and help you to stay motivated and on track. Break large tasks down into manageable chunks:
  - Plan a timetable of when you will do each task.
  - Remember that it might be useful to allocate a larger amount of time to some activities. For example, writing an assignment may be better done in one session so that your ideas flow more easily.
  - Prioritise – don't do the easiest thing first, but the most immediate thing first.

Being flexible

The unexpected always happens, so don't become upset or disheartened if you are unable to stick to your timetable. Ask yourself what needs to be done to get back on track and don't be afraid to ask colleagues, family and friends to support you.

Confidentiality and consent

This book encourages you to relate what you are learning to your work situation. As part of this you will need to reflect on the way you work with people with learning disabilities. Before you involve an individual with learning disabilities in any activities from the book you will need to obtain their consent. Discuss this with your line manager before going ahead.

If you use information about or observations of your colleagues or individuals with learning disabilities in your written work you should be aware of the need for confidentiality. Rather than use someone's real name, you should use a false name or an initial to identify them. You should show the individuals what you have written or tell them about it to check that they are comfortable with what you have written. Discuss your organisation's confidentiality policy with your line manager before completing any of the activities.

Plagiarism

Passing off someone else's work as your own or using someone else's work without acknowledging them is a form of cheating known as plagiarism. Copying other people's work is a serious matter and it is not acceptable to pass off someone else's ideas as your own when you are completing any written work, such as an assignment.

Plagiarism includes:

- copying directly from a book, website, handout or another learner's work
- unfairly using another person's ideas in your work or rewriting a passage from a book or website without saying where you got the ideas from.

You can read books, handouts and information from the Internet when you are studying. To make sure you are not accused of plagiarism when writing an assignment you should always:

- complete it in your own words
- make sure, if you are studying with other people, that you each produce a different assignment
- use quotation marks if you quote directly from someone else's work – for example, 'prejudice means that we have preconceived opinions that are not based on reason'
- acknowledge fully where you obtained your information if you want to quote from a book or article or information you have obtained from the Internet – for example, give the title, author and date of publication and the publisher (for example, see page 61)
- include the web address and the date you obtained the information if you use ideas from a website.

Using the Internet

The Internet contains a wealth of information to help you with your studies. Most of it is extremely valuable. However, some websites contain information that is not reliable. Here are some things to bear in mind when using the Internet for research.

Use only websites that you know to contain reliable information. For example, if you were researching government policies you would go to an official government website. If you wanted information about a particular learning disability you would find it on the website of an organisation that supports people who have that learning disability.

Remember to note down the website address to show where you obtained the information. Do not copy information directly from a website into your own written work without saying where you got it from, as this would be a form of plagiarism.

Do not buy ready-made assignments from the Internet. This is also plagiarism.

Understanding the nature of abuse and neglect

1

'If you see your colleague doing something a certain way, but you don't know any better, who are you to say that it's wrong?'

John Adams, *Support worker*

Introduction

In recent years there have been a number of high-profile cases of abuse of people with learning disabilities. In all of the cases the abuse went on for a long time – sometimes over a period of years. There are different reasons why this happened in each of the incidences, but in some of them lack of staff training about abuse was a significant factor. The enquiry into widespread abuse of people with learning disabilities in the care of Cornwall Partnership NHS Trust in 2006 identified that staff simply did not know that the way they were working with people was abusive. The joint investigation into provision of services for people with learning disabilities at the Trust says the following.

'Although staff were aware of the procedure for reporting abuse, they were largely unaware of what constituted abuse. … In addition, little training and the practice of unqualified staff predominantly learning by observing their peers, has meant that practices, some of which were very poor, have become ingrained.'

CSCI and Healthcare Commission, July 2006

Learning outcomes

This chapter looks at:

- the meaning of the words 'abuse' and 'neglect'
- the types of abuse:
  - o physical abuse
  - o sexual abuse
  - o emotional or psychological abuse
  - o financial abuse
  - o institutional abuse
  - o self-neglect
  - o neglect by others
- signs and indicators associated with these types of abuse.

What is abuse?

rights
a framework of laws that protects from harm, sets out what people can say and do and guarantees the right to a fair trial and other basic entitlements, such as the right to respect, equality, etc.

In *No secrets* (Department of Health and Home Office, 2000) abuse is described as 'a violation of an individual's human and civil **rights** by any other person or persons'. Anyone can experience abuse. It can be a single act or repeated acts. It happens when someone either deliberately or unknowingly causes harm or endangers life or rights.

It is important that everyone who supports people with learning disabilities understands how to recognise abuse and neglect, and how to report it so that it can be stopped and prevented from happening again in the future.

Abuse and power

power
the ability of a person or group of people to exercise authority over another, thereby controlling and influencing others

There is always a link between abuse and **power**. Power exists when one person or group of people has authority over another. By exercising power, people can control and influence others.

In general, people with learning disabilities have very little power in society. They are mostly on the receiving end of events and experiences that happen as a result of how other people exercise their power. For example, many people with learning disabilities find it difficult to access activities and services that others take for granted, such as education, healthcare and employment.

Thinking point
There are people in all our lives who have power over us, such as our doctors or employers. Think about the people in your life who have more power than you. Are there situations in which you feel powerless?

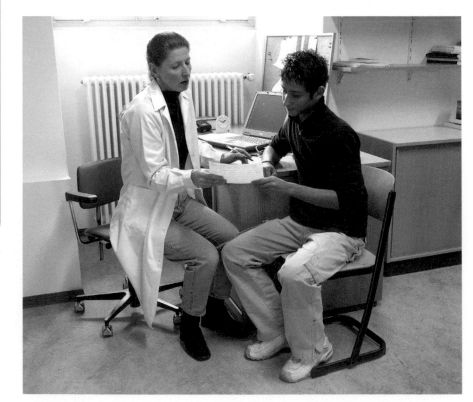

▲ Many jobs put people in a position of power over others.

Power can be used positively or negatively.

If power is used to support people, to bring injustice to light and fight for greater equality, especially in relation to people who experience negative discrimination, it can be a tremendous force for good.

If, on the other hand, power is used simply in order to control people and strengthen the position of a person who is already very powerful, used with little consideration for other people, it is dangerous and harmful.

Don't forget that power is exercised in a variety of different ways, such as by tone of voice, by sarcasm or by the words used.

Abuse is usually the result of power being used in a negative and controlling way. As you read through this book, think about how the types of abuse described below are linked to negative uses of power. Consider how this abuse of power might make it harder for workers to report abusive practices.

Key point
It is important to be able to recognise abuse and neglect so that it can be stopped and so that bad practices carried out by some staff are not passed on to other workers.

Types of abuse

Some things are very easy to identify as abuse. For example, hitting an individual who has a learning disability is obviously physical abuse. However, there are other kinds of abuse which are just as damaging and which you need to be aware of.

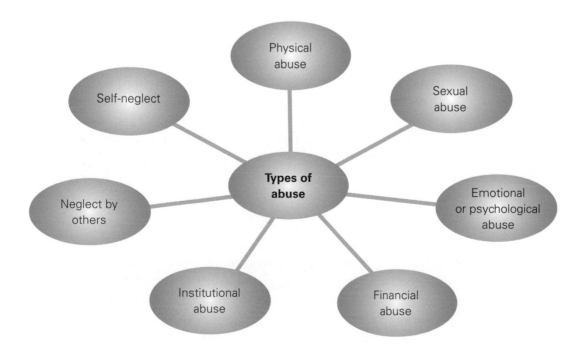

▲ Types of abuse

Physical abuse

Physical abuse includes harming someone by the use of force and applying inappropriate physical force to manage or restrain a person. Your organisation may have a policy that covers behaviour support (the use of physical interventions or physical restraint of an individual by a suitably qualified person) in certain circumstances. This may state, for example, that restraint is permissible if all other attempts to control the behaviour of someone have failed and if the person is acting in a way that is a danger to themselves or to others. If this is the case in your organisation you will have further information and training during or soon after your induction.

Other definitions of physical abuse include:

- using physical force without justification, especially if it results in physical or psychological harm
- leaving someone in a situation in which they experience discomfort or pain, such as sitting on the toilet for a long period of time
- force-feeding someone
- insisting that someone performs a task for which they don't have the energy or ability
- leaving someone in an unheated room or outside the building without being properly dressed
- failing to remove a person from a dangerous situation
- failing to stop someone being physically abused by another person
- threatening violence to get people to do things they don't want to do
- misusing medication to control someone
- inappropriately restraining someone by tying them to a bed or chair, by any means, so that they are unable to move or react
- inappropriately locking someone in a room
- striking someone, pulling their hair or burning with a cigarette.

Sexual abuse

Sexual abuse occurs when one person exerts power over another to achieve sexual gratification. It can include:

- fondling or kissing without consent
- inappropriate intimate touching of a sexual nature by another person including other people with a learning disability
- inappropriately or deliberately encouraging sexual arousal 'just for fun'
- encouraging people to talk about their sexual experiences inappropriately

- making someone do something of a sexual nature against their will
- engaging in a sexual activity with a person with learning disabilities with whom you have a professional relationship
- making pornographic material available inappropriately
- failing to act when you encounter or suspect sexual abuse
- observing sexually inappropriate activities
- encouraging inappropriate sexual relationships between persons with learning disabilities
- taking sexually explicit photographs or electronic images of an individual with learning disabilities
- threatening a person with sexual assault or rape.

Sexual abuse is not always obvious. Some of these activities are only considered abusive if they take place between people where there is an imbalance of power. Services need to support the sexuality of the person with a learning disability and support the rights and choices of the individual while at the same time protecting them from abuse. This can be difficult, as circumstances and individuals vary. Workers supporting people with a learning disability should take care not to prejudge the relationships of those they support, and should ask for advice if they are concerned.

It is a common assumption that staff in services can exercise power over people who use the service. Any sexual contact between a member of staff and a person with learning disabilities is considered abusive.

Some people are unable to consent to sexual activity due to their disability. The Sexual Offences Act 2003 makes it an offence to undertake sexual activity with anyone who does not have the capacity to consent, and makes clear that consent must be freely given. Courts will assume that consent was not given if a person's disability prevents them from communicating whether they want to have sex or not.

Policy reference
Sexual Offences Act 2003

If you or the individuals you support have concerns or queries about sexual abuse, help is available from organisations that deal particularly with sexuality and sexual abuse of people with learning disabilities, such as those listed in Chapter 7.

Emotional or psychological abuse

Emotional or psychological abuse involves acting towards someone in a manner that:

- makes them fearful, upset or unhappy
- causes them undue stress or anxiety
- causes them to act against their will as a result of fear or anxiety.

Examples of emotional or psychological abuse include:

- bullying (negative, aggressive and targeted behaviour carried out over a period of time which can be by a support worker, another person with a learning disability, a family member or someone the individual encounters in the community, such as a member of the public)
- threats or threatening language
- veiled threats, such as 'If you don't do as I say your mother won't visit you this week'
- swearing and shouting
- having no choice about living with someone who is aggressive or threatening
- deliberately discussing experiences that belittle people
- reminding people of their inadequacies and inabilities
- deliberately doing things that will 'wind people up'
- ignoring people for long periods of time
- denying someone's requests, choices, opinions and privacy
- restricting access to friends and family
- ignoring religious or cultural needs.

Financial abuse

Financial abuse involves acquiring money or property by deception or using other people's money or property contrary to their wishes or the wishes of those looking after their interests.

Financial abuse includes:

- theft of money or belongings
- using money intended for one purpose for a completely different purpose, without the free consent of the person concerned
- asking for money for things that ought to be provided as part of the service
- borrowing money from a person with learning disabilities (except in real emergencies, when it should be paid back promptly and correctly documented)
- encouraging people to spend money when they don't want to – for example, accusing them of being 'mean'
- pressurising or deceiving people into financial transactions, such as changing wills or buying inappropriate goods
- sharing one person's money with others without their agreement
- taking advantage of 'offers' when out shopping with a person you support – for example, taking home for personal use the 'free' item from a 'buy one, get one free' promotion, or adding points to a personal store loyalty card without the consent of the person you are supporting.

Scenario: Stephen's money

▲ Stephen gives the money to the stranger without question.

Stephen has autism and so has a tendency to follow instructions literally. He travels to his work placement independently every morning by train. One morning, as he comes out of the station, a stranger asks him for one pound, to buy a cup of tea. Stephen gives the money to her without question. The next morning the stranger is there again and does the same thing, and Stephen again gives her money. The stranger soon discovers that Stephen will give her any amount of money she asks for. Meanwhile, Stephen is becoming disturbed by what is happening, but does not know how to stop it. Eventually, he confides in his support worker, Martin, who accompanies him on his journey the next morning. Martin sees what is happening, warns the stranger about her behaviour, and later helps Stephen develop some strategies for making sure the same thing does not happen again in the future.

Institutional abuse

Institutional abuse is abuse that has become commonplace in a service and that restricts the freedom of people, harms them or denies their human rights.

This sort of abuse usually arises when the smooth running of the service or the needs of the staff are put before the needs of the people with learning disabilities they are there to support. It also occurs when bad work practices have become the normal, accepted way of working, and when nobody appears to question them.

Institutional abuse may include:

- having strict disciplinary rules by which people are controlled, such as only being allowed out with permission
- a lack of individuality among those people supported by the service – for example, where everyone has the same mealtimes and bedtimes, or dresses in a similar way and has a similar haircut
- people having their bags, rooms or person searched
- people being prevented from doing things that are their right
- people's post being read without their permission
- open access to people's rooms without any regard for privacy
- making people leave the bathroom door wide open
- giving medicine to control behaviour so that an individual does not disrupt the smooth running of the service, rather than for valid medical reasons
- making people share clothing with other people.

Neglect by others

neglect
systematic and consistent failure to respond to people's needs

Neglect means systematically and consistently failing to respond to a person's needs or failing to take actions in their best interests. It can be deliberate or it can happen by default, for example, by the support worker failing to check out or anticipate the individual's wishes or needs.

Examples include:

- family members or support workers not passing on essential information to service staff where this will put a person with a learning disability at risk
- leaving someone in bed all day in a residential home because there are staff shortages
- failing to support someone in an activity outside their home because the member of staff doesn't enjoy the activity or doesn't feel like going
- not getting medical attention for someone who is ill
- exposing people to unreasonable risk, such as allowing them to ride in a car without wearing a seatbelt
- not safeguarding people from threats from someone with extreme challenging behaviours
- failing to ensure that people are well equipped for, capable of and suited to any activity that is potentially harmful, such as some sports
- allowing someone to travel around unaccompanied on public transport
- failing to stop someone going off with a person who could harm them
- failing to follow the risk assessment for an individual you support.

Self-neglect

Self-neglect takes different forms. We are all guilty of it to a greater or lesser extent, for instance when we neglect our health needs or don't get enough sleep.

When self-neglect becomes dangerous, we have a duty to do something about it. The kind of self-neglect we are talking about could be when someone:

- puts themselves at risk through failing to take essential medication, for example, for epileptic seizures
- fails to take adequate care of their health
- fails to deal with a potentially harmful illness or injury
- doesn't wear their glasses or hearing aid when they need to
- takes risks with safety, like attempting something dangerous without adequate safeguards or support, or goes out alone after dark to places known to be dangerous.

There are other commonplace situations which, if taken to the extreme, could amount to self-neglect. These include:

- keeping the house in an unsanitary state so that it is a health hazard
- dressing inadequately in bad weather
- failing to wash for long periods to such an extent that their health could be affected and other people could shun them.

Obviously, much of this will depend on the person's abilities and understanding of the risks involved. It is essential to recognise people's right to run their lives as they wish and to respect their privacy. However, if the situation is extreme and there is a danger to the person concerned, the support worker has a duty to act. This should always be done in consultation with the person, unless this is completely impossible, such as if the person is gravely ill or extremely depressed and cannot participate in decision-making. When the self-neglect also puts others at risk there may be a need to act even if the person concerned is unwilling to agree.

There may also be situations where self-neglect is the result of inadequate support or where the person simply cannot manage what is expected of them. In such situations it is neglect by others that is the main problem.

Other types of abuse

It is important to remember that people with learning disabilities may also be the victims of abuse on the grounds of ethnicity, gender or sexual orientation. These types of abuse occur because of prejudice and discrimination towards minority groups in society, not only towards people with disabilities. They are not discussed in detail here, but information about prejudice and discrimination can be found in the publication *Principles of learning disability support*.

Thinking point

Do you ever stay out until the early hours of the morning and get up to go to work a few hours later? Do you feel that you have a healthy diet all the time or are there times when you eat a lot of junk food? Would you ever consider these things to be self-neglect?

Recognising the signs and symptoms of abuse and neglect

It is essential that, as a support worker, you are aware of the signs and indicators of abuse. You must be able to report it, to try to prevent it happening and to play your part in helping people to deal with it. You should be aware, however, that even if you have identified some signs and symptoms of abuse, it does not mean that abuse is definitely taking place. There may be another explanation – so take care not to jump to conclusions.

Signs and indicators of physical abuse

Some of the signs of abuse are common to several types of abuse, while others are more specific.

Some of the common signs and indicators of physical abuse are:

- a person disclosing that they have been physically abused
- flinching or shying away from physical contact
- displaying aggression towards other people
- unwillingness to have any medical attention
- wearing long sleeves, collars or scarves (to cover bruising), even in very hot weather
- being unwilling to take part in activities that involve undressing, such as swimming or sports activities
- being absent from a service or activity regularly with no real explanation
- repeatedly having unexplained bruises, cuts, burns, scalds or bites
- explaining away injuries by saying that they fell or bumped into something
- being afraid of going home
- showing fear of a particular individual.

Signs and indicators of sexual abuse

Some of the common signs and indicators of sexual abuse shown by the person being abused are:

- a person disclosing that they have been sexually abused
- unexplained discharges or bleeding from vagina, penis or rectum
- bruising in intimate areas
- sudden unexplained changes in behaviour
- sudden and frequent mood swings
- becoming very withdrawn
- behaving in an overtly sexual manner
- standing too close and behaving in inappropriate ways with friends or support workers

Thinking point
Think about a time when you have misjudged a situation or jumped to the wrong conclusion about something in your own life. What were the consequences?

Key point
Everyone who supports people with learning disabilities should be able to recognise the signs and indicators of abuse and neglect so that they can report it and play a part in getting it stopped.

- making inappropriate sexual advances to other people
- having much greater difficulty in concentrating than previously
- becoming easily sexually aroused, sometimes for no obvious reason
- becoming very excitable
- becoming preoccupied by sex
- starting to tell you things about sex or ask you questions in a roundabout way, saying they have something private to tell you, but seeming unable to talk about it
- receiving gifts and being unable or unwilling to explain why they have been given
- obsessive behaviour, such as washing compulsively
- being unusually reluctant to have help with personal care
- self-harming, such as cutting themselves
- raising concerns about their own sexuality.

There are other indicators of sexual abuse, shown not by the person being abused but by the abuser. The abuser could be a colleague, another individual who uses the service, a family member or a friend. These signs include:

- a worker showing an inappropriate interest in someone who uses the service
- someone being secretive about their activities with a person who uses the service
- finding someone in a compromising situation with a person who uses the service
- trying to explain away a compromising situation involving a person who uses the service
- a worker sexually harassing someone who uses the service by inappropriate touching or suggestive comments
- a worker spending a great deal of time with a particular person or group of people inappropriately, for example, regularly volunteering to come to work on days off to take a particular individual out
- a worker cultivating a close relationship with a person who uses the service which appears to cross professional boundaries.

It is important to remember that the indicators mentioned above don't necessarily mean that abuse is occurring. However, sudden changes in the way someone acts and extremes of behaviour should always alert you to the possibility that something is wrong.

Signs and indicators of emotional or psychological abuse

Some of the common signs and indicators of emotional abuse are:

- becoming exceptionally withdrawn
- being afraid to say anything for fear of ridicule

- speaking very quietly or in a whisper, sometimes covering the mouth when speaking
- making fun of themselves, but in an excited way, looking for reactions
- appearing to have no emotional reactions to anything
- always shunning company
- constantly seeking reassurance
- being moody and unhappy
- finding it very difficult to get along with other people
- constantly arguing and challenging other people
- having disturbed sleep patterns
- changes in eating patterns, such as going off food or comfort eating.

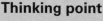

A person who emotionally or psychologically abuses others may:

- shout a lot and use bullying behaviour
- threaten people and try to control their behaviour
- constantly make fun of people and say derogatory things about them
- take delight in making people afraid or making them cry
- find it difficult to relate to people – colleagues as well as the people they support.

It is also important to remember that abusers may not appear to be any different from anybody else and may indeed appear to be charming. This is one reason why abusers are sometimes able to carry out abuse over a long period of time.

Signs and indicators of financial abuse

Many people who have learning disabilities need support with managing their money. People who financially abuse may be deliberately taking advantage of such individuals, or may not realise that what they are doing is financial abuse. When a person is being financially abused one or more of the following may be evident:

- money disappearing without explanation
- someone suddenly acquiring money without explanation
- lack of transparency about the way money is used – some people being 'in the know' about finances and others left uninformed, for example
- large surpluses building up but services being curtailed or of poor quality or in poor repair
- a person's money being spent without their involvement
- property going missing without trace
- a change in appearance, such as someone looking dishevelled when they previously had been smartly dressed
- a lack of food or heating.

Signs and indicators of institutional abuse

An investigation into services for people with learning disabilities provided by a primary care trust in England in 2006 found that institutional abuse was common in most parts of the service. The lifestyles and needs of the individuals were sacrificed in favour of the needs of the service. The Healthcare Commission report of January 2007 said, 'This type of institutional abuse was largely unintentional, but it is abuse nevertheless.'

When abusive practices become the norm in an organisation you may find some or all of these signs:

- staff needs and wishes being put first and the wishes and choices of the people they support not being followed up
- a service being run in a regimented fashion, for example, set mealtimes and bedtimes
- no opportunity for people who use the service to participate in choices or decision-making
- no recognition of cultural or religious diversity
- self-advocacy groups being forbidden or discouraged
- family members and carers being made unwelcome
- people's needs, such as special diets or particular medical needs, being ignored
- punishment being part of the regime
- physical restraint being regularly used as a means of control, with no reference to a person's support plan and without using ways to defuse and manage situations
- an atmosphere of fear and submission in the service
- being charged for things, such as transport, that should be provided as part of the service.

Everyday situations

Here are some situations in which there are signs that abuse may be happening. Remember that just because the signs are there does not mean that the person is definitely being abused.

- Aleesha is normally lively and extrovert. Recently, she has become quiet and withdrawn. When her friend Paul comes to see her she becomes tense and afraid. Aleesha's change in personality and behaviour may indicate sexual, physical or emotional abuse.
- Rob's finances are managed by the manager of the residential home where he lives. His personal allowance is given to him weekly. Recently, Rob has been exhibiting some challenging behaviour, so, as a way of dealing with this, the home manager has told Rob that he can only have his personal allowance if he 'behaves himself' all week. The home manager's actions could be seen as financial abuse. Rob's personal allowance is for him

to spend as he wishes and should not be withheld from him in this way.

- Katherine is wearing a new gold necklace. She is reluctant to tell anyone where she got it from, but eventually tells her support worker that Colin, another support worker, gave it to her. She says that Colin is her boyfriend but he has told her that she shouldn't tell anyone. There are two signs of sexual abuse in this example. A support worker is giving expensive gifts to someone he supports and Katherine has been told by Colin not to tell anyone about the relationship.

Activity 1

Indicators of abuse

Look at the following example and identify the types of abuse that it signals. Remember that just because these symptoms are there does not mean that the person is definitely being abused.

Temi attends St Mary's Church of England church every Sunday. For the past two weeks her support worker has asked her if she minds going to St Francis Roman Catholic church instead as it's nearer and saves time. Temi does not really feel comfortable in St Francis church but she likes her support worker and doesn't want to upset her.

Discuss your answers with your line manager or a senior colleague.

Signs and indicators of neglect

Sometimes it is easy to tell if someone is being abused through neglect, but sometimes the signs are quite subtle. Here are some of the signs that should alert you to the possibility of neglect:

- a person being absent on a regular basis for spurious reasons from their work, day service or college
- people from the same residential service wearing each other's clothes regularly
- a person dressing inadequately for the weather or in ill-fitting or very old clothes while the rest of the family they live with are better dressed
- someone who lives in the family home seeming to do all the chores in the house or being kept at home regularly in order to look after other family members, regardless of their own needs or wishes
- families repeatedly stopping a family member from joining in extra activities or outings, giving no suitable reason

- an individual never seeming to have any money although you know they receive disability allowances or get a wage from work
- an individual not having appropriate access to health care, social care or educational activities
- the support workers who support the individual not seeming to know much about the individual and being unable to provide the support they need.

It can be very difficult to prove abuse through neglect, particularly in the family home. Every family organises life in a way that suits them. Apparent lack of money may just **reflect** a parent being overcautious or not recognising the adult status of their son or daughter. This is not neglect. In fact, it is usually quite the opposite and is sometimes called 'overprotectiveness'. If you suspect that this is happening to someone you support you should inform your line manager, who should be able to identify ways to work in partnership with the family.

> **reflection**
> *careful consideratiion of ideas and issues*

You should now be able to discuss why it is important to recognise the signs and symptoms of abuse and neglect and relate this to your everyday work supporting people with learning disabilities. The following example should help you do this.

Example 1: Signs and symptoms of abuse

For over ten years Edwin has lived in a care home many miles away from his family. He has recently moved back to a new home only three miles away from his mother and older sister and her family. About three weeks after he moved into his new home Edwin's health needs were assessed by his new GP, dentist and local community nurse. They identified that his fingernails and toenails were excessively long, that his feet were in a very poor state and that he had severe tooth decay.

1. Do you think that Edwin may have been abused? If your answer is yes, what type of abuse do you think he may have been subjected to?
2. If Edwin was supported by your service what would you need to do next?
3. Discuss this example with your line manager during supervision or with more experienced colleagues.

Now turn to the commentary on this example on page 54.

2

What makes people with learning disabilities vulnerable to abuse and neglect?

'The more dependent someone is on others for support, and the less control they have over their lives, the more vulnerable to abuse they become.'

Simon Bickerton, *Independent trainer*

vulnerable adult
a person who is or may be in need of community care services by reason of mental or other disability, age or illness and who is or may be unable to take care of themselves or be unable to protect themselves against significant harm or exploitation

Introduction

We are all vulnerable to abuse to a greater or lesser degree. A fit and healthy teenager who has been mugged and had their mobile phone stolen has been physically abused. A business person who has had money regularly stolen from their bank account by a dishonest colleague has been financially abused. Many people say that they have been bullied at school or in the workplace. However, in our society there are some groups of people who are more vulnerable to abuse than others. They are known as **vulnerable adults**.

Learning outcomes

This chapter looks at:

- factors that may make people with learning disabilities particularly vulnerable to abuse and neglect
- factors around particular settings and situations that may create a higher risk of abuse
- the range of people who may abuse individuals with learning disabilities
- reducing the vulnerability of individuals with learning disabilities.

Vulnerable adults

A broad definition of 'vulnerable adult' is in the government report *No secrets*.

> 'A person who is or may be in need of community care services by reason of mental or other disability, age or illness; and who is or may be unable to take care of him or herself, or unable to protect him or herself against significant harm or exploitation.'

You can see from this that 'vulnerable adults' can include people who are elderly or infirm, or physically disabled, as well as people with learning disabilities. However, there are a number of reasons why people with learning disabilities may be particularly vulnerable to abuse.

Policy reference
Department of Health and Home Office (2000) *No secrets: guidance on developing and implementing multi-agency policies and procedures to protect vulnerable adults from abuse* (section 2, page 8)

Dependency on others

Limited understanding of sex

Vulnerability to abuse

Power

Communication

▲ Reasons for vulnerability to abuse

▲ We are all vulnerable to abuse to a greater or lesser degree.

Dependency on others

- Most people with learning disabilities are, to a greater or lesser extent, dependent on others, for example for personal care or to help manage their finances. The more dependent a person is, the more vulnerable they are.
- There is more opportunity to abuse someone who needs help with intimate personal care needs.
- In many 'care' situations, it is easy for an abuser to spend time alone with individuals with learning disabilities.
- People may have limited experience with money and may not be confident with budgeting and handling money, so they are more likely to need support with financial matters.

Limited understanding about sex

- Some people have a limited understanding about sex and so they can't consent to it. They may not understand that sex is different from other things such as having support with intimate personal needs.
- Because of their level of ability and understanding, as well as limited experience, some people may not understand the difference between friendship, a legitimate sexual relationship and sexual abuse.
- The sexual identity of people with learning disabilities is often ignored. People wishing to explore their sexuality may agree to the relationship even if it is an abusive one – they may not understand the notion of abuse.

Communication

- Some people may have difficulty with verbal communication and may be unable to report what is happening, or to say 'no' to the abuser.
- People may not know how to complain about how they are being treated, or other people may not take the complaint seriously or even believe it.
- People who have difficulty in communicating verbally or people with multiple disabilities are at greater risk of being abused physically, financially and sexually.

Power

- Abusers are often people who have some sort of authority over the person being abused. It is difficult for the abused person to speak out against them because they may be frightened or don't know who to tell.
- The abuser may have threatened the person, who may fear that the abuser will carry out their threat if they speak out.

- Many people with learning disabilities have few friends. They may be pleased about receiving attention from someone they like and respect and not realise that they are being abused.

Scenario: Maisie and Demir

▲ Demir tells Maisie he likes her as a friend, but already has a girlfriend.

Maisie is 22 years old and has a learning disability. She is an only child and lives with her parents. She has few friends of her own and rarely goes out without her parents, who are very protective. Maisie would love to have a boyfriend. Her next door neighbour's son Demir is 19 years old. He has known Maisie all his life and often stops to chat to her. Recently, Maisie has developed a 'crush' on Demir. She waits for him to come home from college so she can go out to chat to him and takes every opportunity to visit next door with messages or errands. In this situation it would be easy for Demir to take advantage of Maisie as she is particularly vulnerable to abuse. Instead, he tells her that although he likes her as a friend he already has a girlfriend.

Settings where abuse may take place

Abuse can take place anywhere – in a person's own home, within a residential home or a day-care establishment or in a public place. Some forms of abuse are more likely to happen in certain situations than in others.

Neglect can occur where a service or individual is isolated and where people have limited contact with their local community, family and friends. This could include poor conditions, not giving appropriate medication or the denial of individual freedom.

Activity 2

Settings where abuse may take place

Think about a typical day of someone you support. Make a list of the places the person spends time in that day and note whether the person might be more vulnerable to abuse in some of those settings than in others. Identify the forms of abuse which may be more likely to occur in each of the settings you have identified.

People who abuse

There is a wide range of people who may abuse a person with learning disabilities, including:

- carers, whether relatives or workers in paid employment
- family members or more distant relatives
- friends and acquaintances
- a partner
- staff working with people with learning disabilities, such as day or residential staff, leisure centre workers or colleagues in work placement settings
- volunteer workers
- work colleagues of people with learning disabilities
- people in other positions of authority, such as religious leaders, youth workers or club leaders
- other people with learning disabilities or with other disabilities
- strangers.

It is more likely that an abuser is known to the individual with learning disabilities. In all cases, abuse occurs because there is an unequal power relationship between the person with a learning disability and the abuser.

Reducing the vulnerability of individuals with learning disabilities

Although we have shown that people with learning disabilities are particularly vulnerable to abuse and neglect, there are many ways in which we can work in partnership with people with learning disabilities and their families to reduce their vulnerability. Some of the ways we can do this are as follows.

- Help people understand that they have the right to control their own lives and make their own choices and decisions. For example, help people to make small daily choices, such as what to eat and what to wear, as well as major decisions about where to live and who to live with.

- Challenge situations, circumstances and people who use their power negatively, such as intervening when people with learning disabilities are harassed or bullied by strangers, segregated or barred from establishments, insulted or ignored.
- Give people information they need in a form that they can understand so that they can comprehend their rights and choices about areas such as sex and sexuality.
- Support people to develop the skills they need to stand up for their rights, for example by providing them with assertiveness training.
- Support people to access other sources of help or information, such as an advocate or local advocacy group.

To demonstrate that you have understood the information in this chapter, you should be able to discuss why it is important to know that people with learning disabilities are particularly vulnerable to abuse, and to relate this to your everyday work. The following example should help you do this.

Example 2: Vulnerability to abuse

Steve and Noel are two men in their twenties who are described as having a learning disability. They both attend a part-time horticulture course at their local college. Steve is large and powerfully built. His verbal communication skills are fairly good and he is one of the dominant members of the class. Staff at the college describe him as one of the more able students. Noel is small and slight, has a hearing loss and uses a hearing aid at college. Noel is one of the quieter members of the group. He communicates using a form of sign language called Makaton.

One day, in the lunch break, Steve follows Noel into the toilets. He physically threatens him and sexually assaults him. That afternoon, Noel is so distressed that he is sent home early by the college staff who don't understand why his behaviour has changed so quickly. At home he is most upset. He gradually begins to disclose the assault to his support worker who he knows well and who really understands his signs and gestures.

1. Describe the factors that made Noel vulnerable to abuse.
2. How was the abuse linked to power?
3. What actions could Noel's support worker take to help him be less vulnerable in the future?

Now turn to the commentary on this example on page 55.

Policies and procedures relating to abuse and neglect

'A good procedure should be like a lifebelt. It should support staff to keep afloat. It should be able to offer answers to questions. It should make especially clear how to get help and who to get it from.'

Stephen Dale, *Adult protection co-ordinator*

Introduction

It can be hard to believe that someone who is employed to support a person with a learning disability might harm them but, sadly, this does happen. Sometimes people deliberately target vulnerable people to exploit or harm them, but more often it is because the employee lacks knowledge, understanding or skills. The government has put in place national policies and procedures to safeguard vulnerable adults. These form the basis of the policies and procedures relating to abuse which are put in place by the organisation you work for.

Learning outcomes

This chapter looks at:

- key legislation, national policy and national schemes that relate to protecting people from abuse and neglect
- reports into serious failures to protect vulnerable adults
- the importance of local multi-agency 'protection of vulnerable adults' policies
- organisations' policies and procedures relating to abuse and neglect.

procedure
a set of instructions that sets out in detail how a policy should be implemented and what staff should do in response to a specific situation

Policies and procedures

A policy is a statement of the approach that will be taken regarding particular issues. There are key national policies relating to abuse. Your organisation will also have policies relating to abuse and these will be based on the national guidelines.

A **procedure** is a set of instructions on how the policy should be implemented. Your organisation's procedures relating to protection of vulnerable adults will relate directly to the policy.

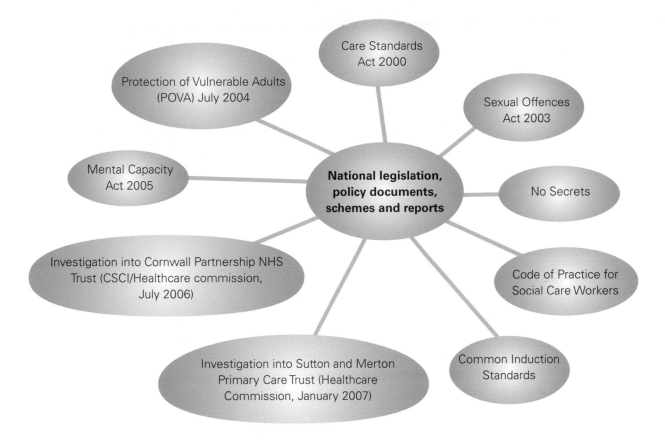

▲ National legislation, policy documents, schemes and reports

Key national legislation

These three Acts of Parliament include safeguards for vulnerable adults.

Care Standards Act 2000

This Act aims to protect vulnerable people from abuse and neglect and to improve the quality of care that people receive. It aims to ensure that older people and people with a disability get appropriate standards of care and the protection they deserve. It introduced the national minimum standards for care, which are used in the inspection of services, and the protection of vulnerable adults scheme.

Sexual Offences Act 2003

This Act changed the law on rape and sexual assault so that offences covered sexual activity with someone who does not have the capacity to consent. The term 'mental disorder' is used in the Act to cover individuals with learning disabilities.

New offences were created:

- Offences against persons with a mental disorder who are unable to consent.
- Inducements, threat and deceptions to persons with a mental disorder.

The offences also apply to workers caring for people with a mental disorder, and strengthen the law as it assumes that care workers understand better than others that the individual could not consent.

Mental Capacity Act 2005

This Act comes into force during 2007 and sets out what should happen when someone lacks capacity to make choices and decisions. The five principles are:

- All adults are assumed to have the capacity to make choices and decisions.
- Everyone should be given all the support and help that they need to make a decision before anyone concludes that they lack capacity.
- People must be allowed to make unwise or eccentric decisions.
- Any actions taken or decisions made on behalf of someone who lacks capacity must be done in their best interests.
- Any decisions made must be those that have the least impact on a person's freedom and rights.

From April 2007, the Act introduces a new criminal offence of ill-treatment or wilful neglect of a person who lacks capacity. If convicted, people can be imprisoned or fined. This covers a failure to provide adequate care, restraining someone unreasonably against their will and any type of abuse or neglect.

Key national policy documents

These policy documents contain national guidelines about safeguarding vulnerable adults. They should inform your organisation's policies on abuse.

No secrets: guidance on developing and implementing multi-agency policies and procedures to protect vulnerable adults from abuse (Department of Health and Home Office, 2000)

It is important for all organisations that might come into contact with vulnerable adults in a local area to work together to develop common policies and procedures. Organisations that should work together include:

- local authority social services departments
- all NHS services in the area
- organisations that provide residential care for vulnerable adults
- organisations providing domiciliary care
- regulators and inspectors of services (currently called the Commission for Social Care Inspection (CSCI) and the Healthcare Commission)
- benefits agencies
- other local authority departments, such as housing
- police
- probation services
- carers' support groups
- groups of people who use services.

The local authority social services department co-ordinates all of this work and produces vulnerable adult protection procedures for the area. You should have a copy in your organisation. If not, you should be able to obtain a copy from your local social services department or download it from your local authority's website. Your organisation will need to follow the vulnerable adults protection procedures for your area in their own policies and procedures.

The Welsh equivalent is *In safe hands: implementing adult protection procedures in Wales* (Welsh Assembly, 2000).

Safeguarding adults (Association of Directors of Social Services, 2005)

This brings together all the good practice which has been developed in adult protection since *No secrets* and offers a national framework of standards for good practice and outcomes in adult protection work.

Code of Practice for Social Care Workers (General Social Care Council, September, 2002)

The code states that as a social care worker you must 'respect the rights of service users while protecting them as far as possible from danger or harm'. In addition, the **General Social Care Council** is the organisation in England with responsibility for the professional registration of all social workers. Eventually it will also register all social care workers. Anyone registered with GSCC who has been found guilty of abuse or neglect is likely to be struck off by the GSCC and unable to work in social care in the future. The equivalent bodies to the GSCC in the other countries of the UK are the Northern Ireland Social Care Council, the Scottish Social Services Council and the Care Council for Wales.

Code of Practice
a UK document for social care workers setting out the standards they should work to

General Social Care Council
the organisation that regulates the social care workforce in England and sets the standards of care through the Codes of Practice

Common Induction Standards (Skills for Care, 2005)

These are the national standards which the induction of all new care workers should follow. The induction that you are undertaking as a new worker specifically includes information about abuse and neglect. This is because it is an important topic that all workers in social care should know about. Your organisation has a responsibility to induct all of its new staff and to include training on abuse and neglect for all staff.

Key national scheme

Protection of Vulnerable Adults (POVA) July 2004

This is part of the implementation of the Care Standards Act 2000. Employers have a duty to report staff members who have been involved in bad practice or abuse, and their names are added to the POVA list. Organisations doing a Criminal Records Bureau (CRB) check on new employees should check against the POVA list at the same time to make sure they are not listed. POVA aims to ensure that people who have been involved in bad practice or abuse of vulnerable adults can never work in social care again.

The Scottish equivalent is PoCSA – Protection of Children (Scotland) Act 2003. There is currently no POVA list in Scotland but legislation is expected. The Northern Ireland equivalent is PoCVA – The Protection of Children and Vulnerable Adults (Northern Ireland) Order 2003.

Reports into serious failures to protect vulnerable adults

Joint investigation into the provision of services for people with learning disabilities at Cornwall Partnership NHS Trust (CSCI/Healthcare Commission, July 2006)

This investigation was started because of serious concerns raised by the East Cornwall Mencap Society about the care and treatment of people supported by the Trust. An investigation was carried out by the Healthcare Commission and CSCI. It found that there were significant failings in the quality and safety of care being provided by the Trust for people with learning disabilities. A number of examples of abuse were highlighted. The report concluded that the welfare of some people was at risk and that urgent action was required to ensure their safety. A number of recommendations were made about changes in the way services were delivered. This enquiry has important lessons for everyone who supports people with learning disabilities.

Investigation into the service for people with learning disabilities provided by Sutton and Merton Primary Care Trust (Healthcare Commission, January 2007)

This investigation took place because the chief executive of Sutton and Merton Primary Care Trust had requested an independent investigation following a number of serious incidents in learning disability services, including allegations of physical and sexual abuse. There were some similarities between the findings in this investigation and the investigation into Cornwall Partnership NHS Trust. One of these was that institutional abuse was widespread but that staff were unaware that what they were doing constituted abuse. As with the Cornwall investigation, changes were suggested to the way services are delivered.

As a result of the Cornwall investigation the Healthcare Commission decided to carry out an audit of learning disability services in England.

Your organisation's policies about abuse and neglect

All organisations should have policies and procedures that help workers to recognise and deal with abuse and neglect. All workers should know where copies of these policies and procedures can be found and what they say. The families of the individuals you support should also know about these policies so that they can be confident that the service will do all it possibly can to protect their relative. People who use the service should have an accessible copy.

Your organisation's policies on abuse should be informed by the legislation and national policies outlined above and clearly describe how the organisation will respond to situations of abuse and neglect. Your organisation's procedures should tell workers what they must do if abuse is suspected or when abuse has been disclosed. The procedures should give the worker clear information about what to do in particular situations.

The policies and procedures in your organisation should include:

- a clear definition of abuse
- guidance for staff on recognising abuse
- details of responsibilities when dealing with abuse
- information on the reporting of abuse and suspected abuse.

Key point
You should make sure that you have read and understood your organisation's policies and procedures relating to abuse and neglect, and that you follow them in your work.

Scenario: Making sure Shafiq is safe

▲ Mr and Mrs Ahmed ask to see a copy of the policies and procedures relating to abuse and neglect.

Mr and Mrs Ahmed and their son Shafiq are visiting an organisation in their area that provides support for people with learning disabilities. They are considering ways in which Shafiq could live more independently. Mr and Mrs Ahmed are aware that their son is vulnerable to abuse, so they ask the organisation if they can see a copy of the policies and procedures relating to abuse and neglect. They are pleased that the policies are clear and detailed and that all staff seem to be aware of them. This helps them to be confident that the organisation will be able to support Shafiq properly and that staff will be able to protect him from abuse.

Activity 3

Policies and procedures on abuse

Find and read through your organisation's policy and procedure on abuse and neglect. If there is anything you are unclear about, ask your line manager. Make notes on the following questions.

- How does your organisation define abuse?
- What steps does your organisation say you should take if you discover or suspect abuse?
- Who should you go to for guidance if you need to discuss an abusive or potentially abusive situation?

Discuss this activity with your line manager at your next supervision.

If your organisation doesn't have a policy on abuse this is a very serious matter. You should talk to your manager about this and you may have to report it to your local council adult social services department or the local CSCI offices.

Every member of staff should be familiar with these documents. Your organisation should regularly review these polices and procedures in the light of national changes in the law and guidance and in the light of experience in using the policies and procedures.

In addition, your organisation has a duty to make sure that the people who use your service:

- know what 'abuse' means
- recognise when they are in danger of any kind of abuse
- know what to do and who to talk to if they are worried about abuse or being abused.

To demonstrate that you have understood the information in this chapter, you should be able to discuss how your organisation's policies and procedures about abuse and neglect relate to your everyday work. The following example should help you do this.

Example 3: Policies and procedures on abuse

Len works in a day service for people with learning disabilities. He is a horticulture specialist. The people who use the service either travel independently each day or are accompanied by a support worker. One morning, as he walks to the entrance to meet his group, Len sees Amina and her support worker Katya coming down the drive. His attention is drawn to them because it appears that Katya is shouting at Amina, and then he watches in horror as Katya slaps Amina across the face.

1. According to the policies and procedures relating to your organisation, what should Len do next?
2. Imagine that an investigation finds Katya guilty of physically abusing Amina. Will she be allowed to work with individuals with learning disabilities in future? Which policy informs this decision?
3. Discuss this example with your line manager or a colleague.

Now turn to the commentary on this example on page 55.

4

Responding to suspected abuse and neglect

'Support workers are vital in recognising abuse and neglect. They spot things managers will never see.'

Neville Parkes, *University lecturer*

Introduction

If you suspect a person you support is being abused or neglected you must act. Policies and procedures, both national and within your organisation, which relate to abuse and neglect state that, as a social care worker supporting vulnerable adults, you have a responsibility to be aware of issues to do with abuse and neglect. You should report any concerns or information you have that someone is, or may be, experiencing abuse.

Learning outcomes

This chapter looks at:

- why it is important to report any suspicions about abuse and neglect
- how, when and to whom you should report suspected abuse or neglect as required by your organisation's policies and procedures
- what to do in the case of suspected abuse or neglect of a child.

The importance of reporting suspicions about abuse and neglect

disclosure
telling someone about abuse they have seen or experienced

If someone **discloses** or tells you about abuse that they have seen or experienced it is clear that you have a duty to report it. However, you may think that something you have seen or heard is so insignificant that it is not worth reporting. This is never the case. Of course, there is a risk that you have misinterpreted what you saw or heard, but there is a much greater risk that you are contributing yourself to someone's abuse by failing to report it. Even if something seems very small, when put together with information from other people it might help to show that abuse is taking place.

The individual who is being abused may not report the abuse themselves, perhaps because they are unable to communicate verbally, may be frightened, may not know how to report it or not realise that they are being abused.

▲ When you share your concerns you may find that others feel the same way.

Your organisation's policies and procedures will stress the importance of reporting suspected abuse and neglect so that:

- the abuse can be stopped immediately
- the perpetrator can be stopped from abusing others
- the person who is being abused can be protected properly and receive help
- the abuser can be held accountable for their actions and measures can be taken to prevent them abusing others.

Reporting suspected abuse or neglect

If someone discloses that they are experiencing abuse you must take it seriously and respond carefully. What you should do is discussed in detail in Chapter 5.

Even if someone doesn't tell you they are experiencing abuse you may suspect that abuse is happening because:

- you are contacted by a relative, friend, member of the public or employee of another organisation to discuss their concerns about possible abuse
- you observe possible abuse taking place
- you notice a number of signs or indicators that someone is being abused – you don't have to wait until you have 'hard evidence'.

Thinking point

Have you ever been concerned about something you have seen or heard, and when you have shared your concerns found that the person you shared them with felt the same way? How did you feel? Did you wish you had talked to them earlier?

How, when and to whom to report suspected abuse or neglect

In your induction as a learning disability worker you will learn about the importance of confidentiality. However, reporting information about suspected abuse does not breach confidentiality and you must not keep it to yourself. If someone tells you that they suspect a person you support is being abused you must make it clear to them that you have to report it, in accordance with your organisation's policies and procedures regarding adult protection. You must report your concerns even if you think that the person who told you their concerns might be unhappy about it. Your policies and procedures will advise you to report abuse to your line manager in the first instance. It will be their responsibility to make sure that the person or people who are at risk of abuse are kept safe.

Scenario: Protecting Lisa

▲ Wen tells Anna that he must tell his line manager what she has told him.

Anna's sister Lisa has a learning disability. Anna is worried because her mother treats Lisa badly. She has seen her hit Lisa, and she shouts and swears at her. Lisa has a support worker, Wen, who takes her out once a week. Anna tells Wen her concerns but asks him not to tell anyone because she is frightened of what her mother will do to her and Lisa. Wen tells her that he must tell his line manager what she has told him and that he has to do this to get the abuse stopped and to protect Lisa from further harm. He reassures her that he will not tell his colleagues or her friends but that he will have to write a report about what she has told him and that his line manager may also want to speak to her.

It is not enough just to pass on the information you have received verbally. You must make a written record of what you have seen or been told as soon as possible after the incident. This is because verbal information can be misinterpreted by the person you are passing it on to. If you do not record the information soon after the event, you may find that you forget some details or that you do not remember exactly what you saw or were told. You should write down:

- when the incident took place or when you were told about the incident
- who was involved and the names of other witnesses, including other people supported by your organisation, colleagues, visitors and family members
- a description of what you saw or were told, making sure that you include as much detail as you can and that you record the facts and not your own interpretation or opinions about what you saw – for example, 'I heard Richard call Morag a "cow". Morag then slapped Richard twice on his left cheek.' not 'Morag was angry because Richard called her a "cow" so she slapped his face.'
- any other information that might be relevant, such as whether there were any previous events that gave you cause for concern.

Key point
Disclosures of abuse do not breach confidentiality. It is your duty to report your suspicions of abuse or any information given to you by another person.

When? When did the incident take place?

Who? Who was involved?

What? What did you see or were you told?

Where? Where did the incident happen?

▲ You must make a written record of what you have seen or been told.

Activity 4

Responding to abuse

Imagine that you think you have just seen a colleague hit one of the people you support. Read through your organisation's policies and procedures again and make notes on the following questions.

- Who should you report this to?
- When should you report your suspicions?
- What should the procedure be after this?

Practice writing a report of the incident, making sure that you have included all the key information and recorded only the facts. Discuss your notes with your line manager.

Responding to suspicion of abuse of a child

Although you may not work directly with children, you have a duty to report any suspicions you have that any child that you come across in the course of your work is being abused or neglected, not just those with a learning disability.

The protection of children is covered separately as a result of legislation following a number of high-profile cases where children were abused and services failed to protect them.

Policy reference

Children Act 2004

Common Induction Standards for Social Care (Adults, England 2004)

The Children Act 2004 amended the Children Act 1989 and placed a duty on local authorities and their partners (including the police, health service providers and the youth justice system) to co-operate to promote the well-being of children and young people and to make arrangements to safeguard and promote the welfare of children.

One of the outcomes from the Common Induction Standards which relates to abuse and neglect is that all new employees should know what to do if they suspect any child is being abused or neglected.

If you suspect any child is being abused, you should follow your organisation's usual policies and procedures for reporting abuse. Your line manager will refer your report to the local authority child protection team who will decide what action should be taken. Further information about the role of the child protection team in your area can be found on your local authority's website.

▲ You can access details about your local child protection team on the Internet.

To demonstrate that you have understood the information in this chapter you should be able to discuss why it important to report any suspicions about suspected abuse or neglect in your work with people with learning disabilities. The following example should help you do this.

Example 4: Responding to abuse

Rachel has recently started a new job as a support worker. Part of her role is to support Yvonne at her cookery class on a Wednesday morning. Yvonne is 19 years old and is described as having severe learning disabilities. She has some limited verbal communication but uses Makaton sign language. Yvonne lives at home with her mother, father and older brother. Rachel is becoming aware that Yvonne's brother has started to behave very negatively towards her. When Rachel picks Yvonne up he makes comments such as 'I don't know why you're bothering to take her – she'll never be able to cook.' One Wednesday morning when Rachel arrives early her brother is shouting at her and Yvonne is crying. Later she notices that Yvonne has severe bruises on her legs. When she asks Yvonne about them she becomes very distressed.

1. What actions should Rachel take?
2. What actions should Rachel not take?
3. Give reasons for your answers.

Now turn to the commentary on this example on page 55.

Responding to a disclosure of abuse

'I kept telling people what was happening but they told me I must be imagining it. Finally, a support worker actually listened to what I was saying and then something was done about it.'

Sarah Jones, *Self-advocate*

Introduction

Disclosure is the term that is commonly used when an abused person tells someone about the abuse. It is most often associated with sexual abuse, but can also refer to other forms of abuse.

When someone makes a disclosure about abuse they are likely to experience a range of feelings. It is important for you to understand the difficulty that disclosure presents for people, and how this can affect those with learning disabilities. The person raising the concern is likely to experience a great deal of fear and confusion and many other feelings. Being aware of how the person might be feeling puts you in a much better position to listen and to provide the support the individual will need throughout the disclosure period and beyond. It is also important that members of the individual's family are also aware of these issues so that they can respond appropriately to a disclosure of abuse.

As a support worker you should take action in response to a disclosure of abuse from a person you support. There are also things you should avoid doing.

Learning outcomes

This chapter looks at:

- the key actions you must take when an individual discloses abuse and why you must do this
- the things that you must avoid doing or saying when someone discloses abuse, and the reasons for this.

Actions to take following a disclosure of abuse

If someone discloses abuse to you it can be difficult to know what to say or do, especially if you are a new or inexperienced worker. It's important to think carefully about your actions so that you support the individual, while at the same time making sure that your actions do not put any future investigation at risk.

Supporting the individual

A person who is disclosing abuse is likely to experience a range of feelings that might include:

- blaming themselves
- being afraid of the consequences of the disclosure
- being afraid of not being believed
- being afraid of making people angry
- relief at the disclosure.

Thinking point
Have you ever been worried about something for a long time without telling anyone? Who did you choose to talk to? How did you feel when you had told them?

 Feelings of person disclosing abuse

It is not easy to support someone who discloses abuse, especially if you have no previous experience of doing so. Here are some practical steps you can take.

- You may need to set aside some time immediately to talk to the person. This means you may have to delay another activity or, if the disclosure occurred near the end of your shift, be prepared to work late.
- Try to stay calm and not to show any feelings you may have, such as shock, anger or disgust. The individual may think that they are upsetting you and not tell you any more.
- Think carefully about what you say. Avoid expressions such as 'You're joking!', or expressing any opinion about what you are being told.
- Reassure the person that:
  - the disclosure will be taken seriously
  - they are not to blame and that the abuse is not their fault
  - the disclosure was the right thing to do.

- Listen carefully and try not to interrupt when someone is telling you their story. Reflect back to the person what they have told you to check that you have understood. If they change their version of events during the discussion you should report both versions.
- Explain clearly to the person what will happen next and that you must pass it on, for example, that you will speak to your line manager, with or without the individual present, depending on how they feel. Your manager will then want to hear about the abuse themselves when the person feels ready to talk about it again. Reassure them that you will be there if that's what they want.
- Explain that you and your line manager will make sure that the abuse is dealt with and that it will stop. Be honest with the individual concerned, saying that it might take time to get everything done and that they might have to speak to some other people, but that you will be there to help whenever they need you.
- Check that the person understands what you have said. You may have to repeat it several times as they may be very emotional and be unable to take in what you are saying at first.
- While you are talking to the person, observe their behaviour and body language. Look for other indicators, such as whether they appear frightened or upset.

Following your organisation's policy and procedure

If someone discloses abuse to you, you must follow your organisation's policies and procedures carefully. These should include:

- completing the records required clearly and accurately
- remembering to include the time and date, and to sign the report
- raising the concern about abuse to the appropriate person, usually your line manager.

Remember your role is to report the abuse. You must not try to carry out your own investigation.

Actions to avoid following a disclosure of abuse

There are a number of actions you should avoid when someone discloses abuse. You could compromise the situation and make it impossible for the concern to be properly investigated. This is especially important if the concern might lead to a criminal investigation.

Unfortunately, people with learning disabilities are already considered to be unreliable witnesses in law. If you ask questions about the abuse you may be seen as having put ideas in their mind or convinced them that they have been abused. If this happens it is unlikely that the investigation can proceed. As it is difficult for cases of the abuse of people with learning disabilities to get to court, support workers or members of the person's family should act properly to make sure they do not inadvertently weaken the case. The way you ask questions is important. You must make sure that you do not 'suggest' to the individual who has disclosed abuse what might have happened or how they might be feeling. For example, instead of saying 'Who gave you that bruise?' you could say 'Would you like to tell me how you got that bruise?' Or, instead of saying 'Did he touch you. That's awful. You must feel dreadful.' you could say 'What happened? How are you feeling?'

In 2001, Mencap, Respond and VOICE produced a joint document relating to the law and the abuse of people with learning disabilities. In it they said the following:

> 'People with a learning disability who have been sexually abused do not receive equal and just treatment within the legal system… Few cases reach court and even fewer result in conviction.'

Change happens slowly. In 2005, the charity Action on Elder Abuse undertook government-funded research into the abuse of vulnerable adults. They found that, out of 639 cases referred to adult protection teams in nine local authorities over a six-month period, only five resulted in prosecution. Therefore, although it is important that you listen and reassure a person disclosing abuse, it is essential not to ask any leading questions about the alleged abuse.

Activity 5

Responding to a disclosure of abuse

The following are some of the kinds of things you should avoid saying when someone discloses abuse. Write down what you think you should say instead.

- It looks as though someone has upset you. Who was it?
- Do you think it was Lisa who took your money?
- Who made you cry?

Discuss your answers with your line manager.

Be very careful not to express anger, even towards the perpetrator, as the person who has disclosed abuse may think you are angry with them. Do not display any disbelief, as this will undermine the person making the disclosure.

You must not confront the alleged abuser, because this is the responsibility of the investigating authorities and you may be giving them time to confront or intimidate the victim, or destroy the evidence. If the matter proceeds to a criminal investigation you will be questioned and may also be required to act as a witness. Any attempt to discuss the abuse with the perpetrator will endanger the investigation.

You should not discuss the alleged or suspected abuse with colleagues, apart from those directly involved, or with the person's family, or your own friends or family. This is a time when confidentiality is paramount. You are likely to need support yourself at this time, but this should be professional support from your line manager or others in your organisation.

In the case of alleged recent sexual abuse, discourage the person from washing, bathing or cleaning their teeth as they may be removing evidence. The police will tell the person when they can wash and change their clothing. You should also leave any other evidence until the police arrive. For example, you should not tidy or clean the area where the incident is alleged to have taken place.

Sadly, incidents of alleged abuse make good stories for the press, and journalists from your local newspaper, radio or TV station may try to contact your organisation. If your organisation has a media policy you should familiarise yourself with it and pass on any enquiries from the press to the appropriate person.

To demonstrate that you have understood how to respond to a disclosure of abuse you should be able to discuss it in relation to your work with people with learning disabilities. The following example should help you do this.

Example 5: Responding to a disclosure of abuse

Michael is a support worker. He works with three people with learning disabilities who live in their own tenancy. One of the people he supports is called Nick and is 25 and described as having a moderate learning disability. One morning Nick discloses to Michael that he doesn't like Stephanie, one of the other support workers. He says that when Stephanie is on sleep-in duty she goes into his room and does 'naughty things'. Nick becomes tearful and says he can't tell you any more. Michael is aware that Stephanie is on duty that afternoon.

1. What actions should Michael take?
2. What should Michael not do?
3. Give reasons for your answers.

Now turn to the commentary on this example on page 56.

Blowing the whistle on bad practices

6

'Whistleblowing isn't snitching or stabbing a person in the back – it's your job.'

Sue Sugars, *Service manager*

Introduction

Despite national and local developments to raise concerns about the abuse of vulnerable adults and to require workers to receive training and information, there are still individuals and organisations that fail to protect people from abuse or neglect. People who speak out about bad practices in the workplace are commonly known as **whistleblowers**. Their actions draw attention to what is happening and hopefully make sure that it stops. A whistleblower is someone who reports bad practices to higher authorities or to people who have the power to investigate and put a stop to those practices. There are whistleblowers in all areas of employment. Most instances of whistleblowing go unnoticed. Many people think they are just doing their job when they report that something is going wrong, and mostly their concerns are addressed. However, sometimes whistleblowers make the news headlines. An example from social care was that of February 2006, when a whistleblower exposed alleged abuse at a care home in Hertfordshire, which made national headlines.

whistleblower
someone who reports wrongdoing or bad practices to higher authorities

Learning outcomes

This chapter looks at:

- why the safety and well-being of individuals who are being supported must always take priority over other considerations
- examples of unsafe practices or resource or operational difficulties that may affect the delivery of safe support
- reporting unsafe practices or resource or operational difficulties
- what to do if you have followed procedures to report suspected abuse, neglect, operational difficulties or unsafe practices and nothing has been done.

Why the safety of people comes first

In society, we all have a moral responsibility to look after one another. However, in your role as a learning disability worker this is formalised and you are said to have a 'duty of care' to the people you support. What this means in practice is that the safety of the people you support must take priority over everything else. This is discussed in more detail in the publication *Your role as a learning disability worker*.

While employees have a responsibility to report abuse or bad practices, there is evidence that, in practice, it can be a very difficult thing to do. Whistleblowers may fear the consequences for themselves from individuals or organisations they are reporting on. If the alleged abuser is a colleague, the whistleblower may be afraid that other colleagues will be hostile towards them or isolate them.

> 'I felt like I'd done something wrong because nobody would speak to me on the unit.'
>
> Whistleblower, reported in research paper 'Blowing the whistle on the abuse of adults with learning disabilities'

If the matter they reported on was about organisational procedures or practices, the whistleblower may fear reprisals from the organisation. For example, they may fear that they might be moved to a different or more challenging work setting or that they may be subject to bullying or harassment.

People who are considering reporting serious cases of abuse or bad practice should be aware that their own lives, the lives of the individuals they support and their colleagues could be disrupted while an investigation is carried out.

Although reporting abuse, neglect or bad practice can be difficult, there is a law that protects whistleblowers. This is the Public Interest Disclosure Act 1998 or 'Whistleblowers Act' which encourages people to speak out about bad practice in the workplace and protects them from victimisation and dismissal for raising their concerns. It protects employees who raise concerns 'in good faith' (i.e. that their concern is genuine and not malicious) and states that if an employee is victimised as a result of their concern they can bring a claim for compensation to an employment tribunal.

Organisations are encouraged to put in place a 'whistleblowing policy' to protect their employees. It is a good idea to make the families of the individuals who are supported aware of the whistleblowing policy so they know that staff will be protected if they speak out about abuse.

Thinking point
Have you ever spoken out about something that you believed to be wrong, either in your personal life or at work? Did you think carefully before you did it? How did you feel?

Policy reference
Public Interest Disclosure Act 1998 ('Whistleblowers Act')

Unsafe practices

In the first two chapters we looked at types of abuse and the signs and symptoms associated with these. Generally speaking, an employee should report any incidents of abuse under their organisation's Protection of Vulnerable Adults (POVA) policy. However, there may be situations that do not appear to fit into the categories of abuse which were described in those chapters, but that occur over a period of time, and that the worker may feel uncomfortable about. These are described as 'unsafe practices', and should also be reported.

Examples of unsafe practices include:

- staff who are poorly trained or untrained in specialist areas, such as in working with people with autism, in supporting people with behaviour that could be called challenging or in administering medication
- where staffing levels are very low, such as where a person who uses the services presents very challenging behaviour and the staffing level is consistently below the level that was agreed to keep that person and others safe
- an organisation employing staff to 'sleep in' in a service when the person who is being supported should have a worker who is awake at night either because of their behaviour or their health needs
- individual members of staff who are habitually late for their shift, compromising the safety of the individuals they support.

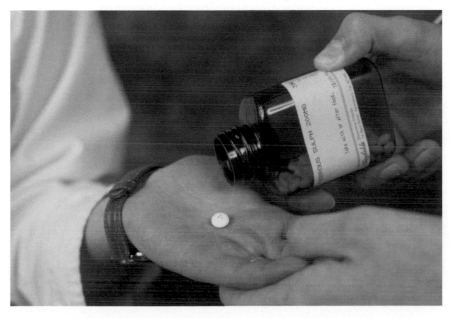

▲ In order to prevent unsafe practices, as above, staff should be properly trained in specialist areas such as administering medication.

Scenario: Supporting Paul safely

▲ The manager regularly asks Dave to go out on his own with Paul.

Paul is described as having challenging behaviour. In his support plan it states that two support workers should accompany him when he goes out. This is to make sure that Paul, the support worker and members of the public are kept safe. However, due to staff sickness there have not been enough support workers available for two people to accompany Paul when he goes out. Paul is an active man who likes to be out in the community and quickly becomes bored if he cannot go out. The manager of the home regularly asks one of the support workers, Dave, to go out on his own with Paul. He says Dave has a good relationship with Paul and knows what to do if Paul's behaviour becomes challenging. Dave is concerned about the consequences for himself and Paul if something goes wrong.

Resource and operational difficulties

Abuse can occur because staff are not properly trained or have acquired sloppy habits or poor ways of working. This can sometimes be because of inadequate supervision or management.

Examples of resource and operational difficulties that should be reported include:

- visits or details of support given not being recorded accurately
- neglecting individuals who have communication difficulties, for example 'forgetting' to offer someone who has profound learning disabilities a drink because they are not able to communicate their needs and wishes verbally
- neglecting the hygiene of the person's environment, or leaving jobs for colleagues to do, for example leaving damp or soiled sheets on a bed in the morning so that the worker supporting the person when they go to bed has to change them
- using equipment or aids that are unsuitable or even dangerous, for example wheelchairs or hoists that are not appropriate for the needs of the person
- poor management or inadequate training, leading to difficulties in the running of the service.

How to report unsafe practices

Most policies will suggest that you report your concerns in the first instance to your line manager or, if your line manager is implicated by the concern you have raised, to a senior manager within the organisation. In most cases the manager will be pleased that you have reported your concerns and will take action informally to make sure the bad practices stop. However, as we have seen, reporting a serious case of bad practice can be a very difficult thing to do and can have serious consequences for the organisation and all the people involved.

Before you raise your concerns, you should think carefully about what might happen as a result of your actions. You should also remember that you are a 'witness', reporting something that has happened to somebody else, not to you. This means that your role is only to report your concerns, not to investigate them. You should not use the whistleblowers policy to pursue a personal grievance. If you feel that you have been badly treated by your employer, you will need to follow your organisation's grievance procedure, not the whistleblowers policy.

Key point
It is your responsibility to report unsafe practices. Although this may be difficult, you are protected by the law.

Most whistleblowing policies suggest that you may like to seek the advice and support of someone independent before you raise your concern. For example, the organisation Public Concern at Work offers free advice to people who have raised, or are considering raising, concerns, and they can offer more help if they are contacted at an early stage. You might also contact your union representative, someone from your personnel department or simply ask a friend to offer you support, but without discussing confidential details, such as the names of the people involved or the work setting.

Activity 6
Whistleblowing

Read a copy of the whistleblowing policy for your organisation and check that you understand it. How and to whom should you report any concerns about abuse, neglect or unsafe work practices?

Discuss the policy with your line manager if there are any points you are unclear about.

What to do if nothing is done

If you have followed your organisation's procedures to report abuse, neglect, unsafe practices or operational difficulties and you feel that nothing has been done or nothing changes, then most whistleblowing policies advise you to report your concerns to an external body. For people who work in learning disability services this is probably the regulation and inspection service (currently the CSCI), which is likely to regulate the service you work in. This is a very serious step to take. You should make sure you seek independent advice before you do this. As a witness you would not have been kept informed about the progress or outcome of any investigation that has taken place, and you should bear in mind that actions may have been taken without your knowledge.

To demonstrate that you have understood the information about reporting your concerns about abuse or bad practices you should be able to discuss how you would apply this to your work supporting an individual with learning disabilities. The following example should help you do this.

Example 6: Whistleblowing

Surjinder is a support worker who supports Junior with personal care for two hours each day during the week – one hour in the morning and one hour at night. Another support worker, Avril, supports him at weekends. Junior has a diary in his flat in which the support worker records their arrival and leaving time. Junior is unable to read and write but he knows that the people who support him need to sign the book. Surjinder begins to be concerned that at the weekends Junior is not receiving the level of support that he should. When he arrives on Monday morning it appears that Junior has not had a shave or a bath over the weekend and is wearing the same clothes Surjinder helped him choose last Friday. When Surjinder asks Junior whether Avril has visited him he says that she has visited each day, and when he checks the diary he finds that Avril has signed it to say that she has supported Junior for two hours each day. Surjinder is still concerned, so when he meets Avril in the office he asks her in passing how she thinks Junior is doing at weekends. Avril says, 'Well I just pop in in the mornings to check he's OK. He can look after himself fine and it's the weekend – he needs a break!'

1. What actions should Surjinder take?
2. What should he avoid doing?
3. How is Surjinder protected in law?
4. Avril is clearly in breach of her contract here. Can you list the reasons why?

Now turn to the commentary on this example on page 56.

7 Getting further information and advice

'Abuse is a very wide area. Sometimes it's hard to know whether something you are doing is committing an abuse.'

Paula Robbins, *Support worker*

Introduction

Abuse is a very difficult subject. There may be signs and symptoms of abuse but these may not necessarily mean that abuse is occurring. It is part of your job to report suspected abuse, but this can be hard. It is important to support someone who has disclosed abuse to you, but at the same time you must be careful what you say or do so that you do not damage any case that may be brought against the alleged perpetrator. It is not surprising, therefore, if there are situations where you feel you need further information and advice about abuse and neglect.

Learning outcomes

This chapter looks at:

- factors that would lead you to access further information and advice about protecting people who have learning disabilities
- sources of information and advice about your role in the protection of people who have learning disabilities and how to access them.

When further information is needed

You may find yourself in a situation in which you think abuse might be occurring but you are not sure. For example:

- when you observe a colleague treating someone they are supporting in a way that seems to you to be abusive, but you are not sure, such as pushing someone roughly
- when you are not sure whether an action you have taken or plan to take might be considered to be abusive, such as planning to limit the choice of food available to an individual because they have been advised to lose weight

- when you are told something that makes you suspect that abuse is occurring, such as when a friend of someone you support suggests in a roundabout way that the person's money is being used by other members of the person's family.

Sources of information and advice

You can get information and advice from a variety of sources including organisations, websites, publications and the people you work with.

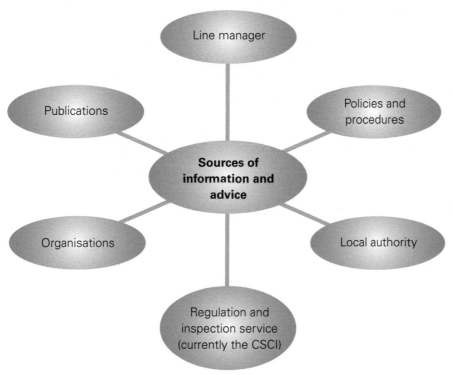

▲ Sources of information and advice

Your line manager

Your line manager is likely to be an experienced worker with knowledge of issues around abuse and neglect and should therefore be a good source of information and advice. It is also important for them to be aware of your progress as they are responsible for what is happening in the service they manage. You can check with your line manager whether the way you are doing things is correct or not. Your supervision session would be a good time to do this.

Scenario: Supporting John

▲ Manjula talks over her concerns with her line manager.

Manjula is a new support worker in a residential care home. She is concerned because she finds it difficult to relate to John, who is one of the residents. She feels that he does not respond when she speaks to him, even when she asks him if he would like a drink or to participate in an activity. She is worried that when she is working John may feel that he is being neglected. Manjula talks over her concerns in supervision with her line manager who suggests some ways in which she could work with John to improve the communication between them.

Policies and procedures

All organisations should have policies and procedures on abuse and neglect. Your organisation's policies and procedures should set out clearly how things should be done. It is a good idea to refer to these.

Local authority

You may feel unable to talk to your line manager or raise your concerns with the organisation you work for. You may also have a more general query about the protection of vulnerable adults. In these cases you can contact your local authority, which will have a department responsible for social care and health that includes specialists on adult protection. You should be able to find the number in the phone book and information on their website.

Regulation and inspection service (currently the CSCI)

The CSCI is the organisation that regulates social care in England. Anyone who is concerned about abuse can make a report directly to it if they don't feel that their concern would be dealt with properly within their own organisation. The Commission is also an important source of information about protection of adults. The equivalent organisation for Wales is the Care Standards Inspectorate for Wales (CSIW), for Scotland the Scottish Commission for the Regulation of Care and for Northern Ireland the Department of Health, Social Services and Public Safety.

Organisations offering information and advice about abuse of people with learning disabilities

There are many organisations that offer advice about abuse to people with learning disabilities, support workers, families and professionals in the field of learning disabilities. These include charities and government departments.

- The Ann Craft Trust is a national charity working with professionals in the statutory, independent and voluntary sectors to protect children and adults with learning disabilities who may be at risk from abuse. They provide advice and information to parents and carers who may have concerns about someone they are supporting.
- VOICE UK is a national charity supporting people with learning disabilities and other vulnerable people who have experienced crime or abuse. They also support their families, carers and professional workers.
- Respond is a charity that supports people with learning disabilities, their families, carers and professionals affected by trauma and abuse. They provide a range of services to both victims and perpetrators of sexual abuse who have learning disabilities and those who have been affected by other trauma.
- Mencap is a UK charity that campaigns for equal rights for children and adults with a learning disability and offers a variety of services to them, their families and carers.

Organisations offering information and advice to people with learning disabilities, their families and people who support them

A number of organisations are experienced in giving advice to people with learning disabilities as well as their families and carers. These include:

* the British Institute of Learning Disabilities (BILD), which is a UK charity committed to improving the quality of life for people with a learning disability

* the Association for Real Change (ARC), which is the UK umbrella for agencies providing any service for people with a learning disability.

Organisations offering information and advice about whistleblowing

Public Concern at Work is an independent authority on public-interest whistleblowing, which promotes compliance with the law and good practice and offers free advice to people concerned about danger or malpractice in the workplace but who are unsure whether or how to raise the matter. The unions UNISON, T&GWU and GMB may also be able to offer information and advice.

Publications about the protection of vulnerable adults

A number of publications deal with issues surrounding the protection of vulnerable adults. Some of these are listed in the resources section on page 61.

Activity 7

Sources of information and advice

Pamela, an individual you support, tells you that she was the victim of sexual abuse some years ago. Although the perpetrator was brought to justice, Pamela still suffers from depression and has nightmares about the abuse.

Identify two organisations you could contact to get advice about support and counselling for Pamela.

You should now be able to demonstrate that you have understood when and where to get advice about protecting people from abuse. The following example should help you do this.

Example 7: Getting advice

Anna is a new support worker at a small residential home for three adults with learning disabilities. As she completes her induction training she becomes more aware of the ways in which she is expected to relate to the individuals she supports. She also begins to become uncomfortable about the actions of one of the senior workers, Jean, which seem to be at odds with what she is learning on her training. For example, she has often observed Jean going into people's rooms without knocking, or taking visitors into people's rooms without their permission. When one of the residents asks her for support going to the toilet, Jean often makes them wait until she has finished what she is doing before she helps them, even when it is something that could be left for a few minutes.

Anna is not sure whether Jean's actions are abusive or whether they are poor practice which should be addressed by the manager. Anna is reluctant to speak to the home manager about her concerns as Jean often gives her a lift home and appears to be good friends with her.

1. Where could Anna find further information and advice?
2. Do you think that Jean's actions are poor practice, or are they abuse?
3. What action, if any, should Anna take?

Now turn to the commentary on this example on page 56.

Commentaries on the examples

At the end of each chapter there is an example and a set of questions for you to answer. The commentaries below highlight the issues that you could have included in your answers. Not everything that can be said about the examples is included. This would take a chapter for each study on its own. They are designed only to act as guidelines on how to approach each situation, and examples of how you can use your own practical experiences to describe and comment on your day-to-day experiences.

If you are taking the Induction Award, you'll find that you are asked to describe situations and give examples using your own experience. Familiarity with working on examples will help you with this, although it is how you present and discuss your own practical experience that counts in the end.

Example 1: Signs and symptoms of abuse

Edwin has probably not been abused, but rather he has been neglecting himself.

The support worker should not:

- cut Edwin's toenails and fingernails for him, either with or without his consent
- book a dental appointment or ask a dentist to visit him without his consent
- ignore the situation – at worst Edwin may be diabetic and need specialist medical help with regard to foot care, or he may have a fungal infection.

The support worker should:

- make sure that Edwin understands the importance of visiting a dentist and a chiropodist by talking to him on several occasions about it so that he begins to understand the possible consequences of neglecting his personal care
- obtain accessible leaflets about oral care and nail care and look at them together with Edwin to aid his understanding
- support Edwin, if he agrees, to make appointments with the chiropodist and dentist
- support Edwin to visit the chiropodist and dentist if he agrees
- keep monitoring the situation and if necessary gently remind Edwin about his personal care.

Example 2: Vulnerability to abuse

Noel was vulnerable to abuse because:

- he had a severe learning disability
- he was physically smaller than his abuser
- he did not communicate verbally so it is likely to have been harder for him to disclose the abuse.

The abuse was linked to power because:

- Steve was physically more powerful than Noel
- he was intellectually more able than Noel and had targeted him because he guessed that Noel would be unlikely to fight back or to disclose the abuse.

To help Noel become less vulnerable in future his support worker could:

- make sure he has access to counselling to assist in his recovery from this incident of abuse
- support Noel to join a local advocacy group
- make sure he has access to alternative methods of communication, such as symbols or pictures, and encourage him to use these to let people know his wishes and feelings.

Example 3: Policies and procedures on abuse

Most organisations, policies will require Len to report what he has seen to his line manager and make a written report.

If Katya is found guilty her name will be added to the POVA list, which will effectively disqualify her from working with vulnerable adults in the future. The policy which informs this is the Protection of Vulnerable Adults, part of the implementation of the Care Standards Act 2000.

Example 4: Responding to abuse

Rachel should report her concerns directly to her line manager. She should report only the facts and not her own interpretation of them. She should also make a written report of what she has seen and been told.

On no account should Rachel confront Yvonne's brother or any other family member. She risks tipping off the abuser and will prejudice any case the police might want to bring later. She may also be putting herself and Yvonne at serious personal risk.

Example 5: Responding to a disclosure of abuse

Michael must report Nick's disclosure to his line manager immediately so that they can take steps to ensure that Stephanie does not come into work that afternoon. He must tell Nick that he has to tell his line manager what Nick has said. He should reassure Nick that what he has said will be taken seriously and he will not get into trouble. He should listen to anything else Nick says. He must write a report of what was said.

He should try not to display any emotions. He should make sure he does not ask Nick leading questions such as, 'What do you mean by naughty things?', but should rather say something like, 'I can see you're upset. Do you want to talk some more?'

Michael must not ignore or dismiss Nick's disclosure. He must not tell Stephanie about the disclosure. He must not discuss it with other colleagues or his friends and family.

Example 6: Whistleblowing

Surjinder should report his concerns to his line manager. He should give the evidence to back up his concerns. He should not challenge Avril himself. Surjinder has a duty to report his concerns in order to protect Junior. As he is not making malicious allegations just to get Avril into trouble he is protected by the Public Interest Disclosure Act 1998.

Avril is in breach of her contract for several reasons.

- She is not working the hours for which she is claiming payment so she is defrauding the organisation she works for.
- She is not following the support plan that has been agreed with Junior – it isn't her job to make assumptions about the level of support that he needs at weekends.
- She is neglecting Junior.

Example 7: Getting advice

Although ideally Anna should talk to her line manager, this is going to be difficult if she thinks she is friends with Jean. She could go to a senior manager within the organisation or seek advice from the social services department of her local council.

Going into people's rooms without knocking or taking visitors in without asking are examples of poor practice. However, making someone wait to go to the toilet until the support worker is ready is an example of institutional abuse. Anna has a duty to report her concerns so that the abuse and poor practice can be stopped.

Glossary

abuse a violation of a person's human rights by any other person or persons. Anyone can experience abuse. It can be one single act, or repeated acts. It happens when someone either deliberately or unknowingly causes harm or endangers life or rights

Code of Practice a UK document for social care workers setting out the standards they should work to

confidentiality concerning things that need to be kept private

direct payments a way for people to organise their own social care support by receiving funding direct from their council, following an assessment of their needs

disclosure telling someone about abuse they have seen or experienced

family carer a relative of a person with learning disabilities who has an interest in their well-being

General Social Care Council the organisation that regulates the social care workforce in England and sets the standards of care through the Codes of Practice

induction a period of learning, shortly after starting a new job or volunteering placement, about how to provide good support to people with learning disabilities

neglect systematic and consistent failure to respond to people's needs

policy a statement or plan of action that clearly sets out an organisation's position or approach on a particular issue and tells staff what should be done in the circumstances

procedure a set of instructions that sets out in detail how a policy should be implemented and what staff should do in response to a specific situation

power the ability of a person or group of people to exercise authority over another, thereby controlling and influencing others

reflection careful consideration of ideas and issues

rights a framework of laws that protects from harm, sets out what people can say and do and guarantees the right to a fair trial and other basic entitlements, such as the right to respect, equality, etc.

service the provision of social care support for a person, which could be in their own home, their local community or in a residential home or similar place

vulnerable adult a person who is or may be in need of community care services by reason of mental or other disability, age or illness and who is or may be unable to take care of themselves or be unable to protect themselves against significant harm or exploitation

whistleblower someone who reports wrongdoing or bad practices to higher authorities

Mapping to NVQ Health & Social Care Knowledge Specifications

Chapter 1: Understanding the nature of abuse and neglect

HSC24		HSC240	
9, 11, 12, 15, 17, 19		5, 6, 9	
HSC35	**HSC335**	**HSC395**	
3, 7, 11, 12, 15, 17, 19	3, 6, 10, 11, 13, 14, 20, 21, 22, 23	3, 6, 10, 11, 13, 14, 20, 21, 22, 23	
Links to other units: HSC22, HSC32, HSC329, HSC330, HSC336, HSC3114			

Chapter 2: What makes people with learning disabilities vulnerable to abuse and neglect?

HSC24		HSC240	
2, 5, 8, 12, 14, 15		2, 4, 11	
HSC35	**HSC335**	**HSC395**	**HSC3114**
2, 6, 12, 15, 16, 17, 23	2, 3, 5, 14, 16, 21	2, 3, 5, 14, 16, 21	13, 14, 15, 18

Chapter 3: Policies and procedures relating to abuse and neglect

HSC24		HSC240	
2, 8, 9, 10, 11, 16, 18, 19		1, 4, 5	
HSC35	**HSC335**	**HSC395**	
1, 6, 7, 8, 11, 18, 20	1, 5, 6, 7, 9, 10, 11, 19	1, 5, 6, 7, 9, 10, 11, 19, 27, 28	
Links to other units: HSC22, HSC32, HSC329, HSC330, HSC3114			

Chapter 4: Responding to suspected abuse and neglect

HSC24		HSC240	
2, 9, 13, 16, 18, 21		1, 2, 4, 5, 12	
HSC35	**HSC335**	**HSC395**	
2, 4, 6, 7, 8, 18, 20, 21	1, 2, 3, 5, 6, 7, 17, 19, 25, 26	1, 2, 3, 5, 6, 7, 17, 19, 25, 27, 28	
Links to other units: HSC22, HSC32, HSC329, HSC330, HSC3114			

Chapter 5: Responding to a disclosure of abuse		
HSC24		**HSC240**
2, 5, 6, 8, 9, 13, 16, 18, 21		2, 5, 8, 12
HSC35	**HSC335**	**HSC395**
2, 3, 4, 7, 8, 16, 18, 20, 21, 23	1, 2, 3, 6, 7, 11, 17, 19, 24, 25, 26	1, 2, 3, 6, 7, 11, 17, 19, 24, 25, 27, 28
Links to other units: HSC22, HSC32, HSC329, HSC330, HSC3114		

Chapter 6: Blowing the whistle on bad practices		
HSC24		**HSC240**
2, 8, 9, 13, 15, 16, 18, 20		1, 2, 4, 5, 6
HSC35	**HSC335**	**HSC395**
1, 2, 3, 6, 7, 8, 17, 18, 20	1, 2, 3, 5, 6, 7, 11, 18, 19, 21	1, 2, 3, 5, 6, 7, 11, 18, 19, 21, 27, 28
Links to other units: HSC22, HSC32, HSC329, HSC330		

Chapter 7: Getting further information and advice			
HSC24			
11, 19			
HSC35	**HSC335**	**HSC395**	**HSC3114**
10, 11	9, 10	9, 10	9, 10, 18

Resources

Publications

Association of Directors of Social Services, 2005. *Safeguarding Adults: A National Framework of Standards for good practice and outcomes in adult protection work*

*Behind closed doors: preventing sexual abuse against adults with a learning disabilit*y, London, Mencap, 2001

Calcraft, R, 2005. *Blowing the whistle on the abuse of adults with learning disabilities.* Ann Craft Trust

CSCI/Healthcare Commission, July 2006. *Joint investigation into the provision of services for people with learning disabilities at Cornwall Partnership NHS Trust*

Department of Health and Home Office, 2000. *No secrets: guidance on developing and implementing multi-agency policies and procedures to protect vulnerable adults from abuse*

Healthcare Commission, January 2007. *Investigation into the service for people with learning disabilities provided by Sutton and Merton Primary Care Trust*

Mental Capacity Act 2005, London: The Stationery Office

Useful websites

Ann Craft Trust: www.anncrafttrust.org

Association for Real Change (ARC): www.arcuk.org.uk

British Institute of Learning Disabilities (BILD): www.bild.org.uk

Mencap: www.mencap.org.uk

Respond: www.respond.org.uk

VOICE UK: www.voiceuk.org.uk

Index